11+
Verbal Reasoning
Cloze

TESTBOOK 2

Cloze Tests

Dr Stephen C Curran

with Warren Vokes

Edited by Katrina MacKay & Andrea Richardson

R _ B _ _ T

This book belongs to

TUITION

Accelerated Education Publications Ltd

Guidance Notes for Parents

Cloze procedure involves supplying missing words or parts of words that have been deleted from a portion of text. Cloze tests require the ability to understand context and vocabulary in order to identify the correct words or parts of words that belong in the deleted passages of text.

Cloze passages include various forms of text:
- **Historical**
- **Biographical**
- **General Knowledge**
- **Literary Text - Prose**
- **Literary Text - Poetry**

There are three question types:

- **Missing Letters**

  In Missing Letters style questions the Cloze passage has a number of words where letters have to be provided to complete the word.

- **Multiple-choice**

  In Multiple-choice style questions there are three alternatives for the missing word in the Cloze passage.

- **Word Bank**

  In Word Bank style questions there are a number of alternatives provided in a set of words at the top of the page. Words are chosen from this Word Bank to fill the spaces in the Cloze passage.

Marking and Feedback
- The answers are provided at the back of this book.
- Only these answers are allowed.
- One mark should be given for each correct answer.
- Do not deduct marks for wrong answers.
- Do not allow half marks or 'the benefit of the doubt', as this might mask a child's need for extra help in the topic.
- Always try to be positive and encouraging.
- Talk through any mistakes with your child and work out together how to arrive at the right answer, using a dictionary if necessary.

Cloze Test 1

Choose the correct words from the word bank below to complete the passage.

brink	**sailing**	**flowers**	**rose**	**mellow**
float	**twilight**	**barley**	**swan**	**clouds**

What is pink? a **1)** _____ is pink

By the fountain's **2)** _____ .

What is red? a poppy's red

In its **3)** _____ bed.

What is blue? the sky is blue

Where the clouds **4)** _____ through.

What is white? a **5)** _____ is white

6) _____ in the light.

What is yellow? pears are yellow,

Rich and ripe and **7)** _____ .

What is green? the grass is green,

With small **8)** _____ between.

What is violet? **9)** _____ are violet

In the summer **10)** _____ .

What is orange? why, an orange,

Just an orange!

What is pink? by Christina Rossetti (1830-1894).

Score ☐ Percentage ☐ %

Cloze Test 2

Select the correct words to complete the passage below.

Born in Paddington in 1857, Robert Baden-Powell was the **1)**
- ☐ founder
- ☐ product
- ☐ ruler

of the

Scouting movement. He **2)**
- ☐ forfeited
- ☐ damaged
- ☐ pursued

a career in the military and was the

garrison commander at the Siege of Mafeking. Following the **3)**
- ☐ started
- ☐ lifting
- ☐ remains

of the

siege, he was **4)**
- ☐ promoted
- ☐ reduced
- ☐ demoted

to Major-General and became a **5)**
- ☐ statutory
- ☐ revered
- ☐ fallen

national hero. On his return from Africa in 1903, Baden-Powell **6)**
- ☐ learnt
- ☐ doubted
- ☐ thought

that

his military training **7)**
- ☐ schedule
- ☐ exercise
- ☐ manual

, *Aids to Scouting*, had become a best-seller,

and was being used by teachers and youth **8)**
- ☐ organisations
- ☐ employers
- ☐ councils

. He decided to

re-write *Aids to Scouting* to **9)**
- ☐ test
- ☐ relish
- ☐ suit

a youth readership. In August 1907 he held

a camp on Brownsea Island to test out his **10)**
- ☐ ideas
- ☐ tents
- ☐ recipes

. The first book on the

Scout Movement, Baden-Powell's *Scouting for Boys* was published in six

11)
- [ ] episode
- [ ] years
- [ ] instalments

in 1908, and has sold 12)
- [ ] approximately
- [ ] exactly
- [ ] under

150 million copies

as the fourth best-selling book of the 20th century. In January 1912, while

13)
- [ ] returning
- [ ] flying
- [ ] en route

to New York on a Scouting World Tour, he met Olave St. Clair

Soames. They became 14)
- [ ] friends
- [ ] rich
- [ ] engaged

in September of the same year, causing a

media 15)
- [ ] sensation
- [ ] blizzard
- [ ] flop

due to Baden-Powell's fame, and married in private on 30

October 1912. The Scouts of England each 16)
- [ ] charged
- [ ] donated
- [ ] received

a penny to buy Baden-

Powell a wedding gift, a car. In 1920, the 1st World Scout 17)
- [ ] Jamboree
- [ ] Circus
- [ ] Fair

took

place in Olympia in West Kensington, and Baden-Powell was 18)
- [ ] exonerated
- [ ] excused
- [ ] acclaimed

Chief Scout of the World, in 1929. Baden-Powell died in 1941. His gravestone

19)
- [ ] creates
- [ ] hides
- [ ] bears

a circle with a dot in the centre "☉", which is the 20)
- [ ] road
- [ ] new
- [ ] trail

sign

for "Going home", or "I have gone home".

Score [ ] **Percentage** [ ] **%**

Cloze Test 3

Choose the correct words from the word bank below to complete the passage.

bankrupt	**efficiency**	**aptitude**	**credited**	**employed**
ingenuity	**original**	**hauled**	**exploit**	**adaptation**

Richard Trevithick, born in Redruth in 1771, was a mining engineer who invented many **1)** _____ machines. They include the screw propeller; the iron ship; a steam carriage; a steam-powered barge; and the first full scale steam-powered locomotive. James Watt is **2)** _____ with the invention of the steam engine, but his was a low-pressure engine. Trevithick's design was driven by high-pressure steam, thereby increasing its power and **3)** _____ . His first steam engine was used, from 1802, at an ironworks in Merthyr Tydfil, to drive a steam hammer, but his **4)** _____ enabled him to see that the engine could be **5)** _____ to power a transport system. In 1804, Trevithick adapted the basic single-cylinder engine with a flywheel arrangement by adding a draught-improving combined steam exhaust and chimney. This **6)** _____ set the standard for all future steam locomotives. Using a metal track, the engine **7)** _____ five wagons, containing ten tons of iron ore and 70 passengers, a distance of ten miles in a trip that took just over four hours to complete. Unfortunately, Trevithick's engineering talent was not matched by any commercial **8)** _____ . He died in 1833, **9)** _____ and in debt. However, he gained a place in history with his greatest achievement: he had laid the foundation for the first use of steam locomotives that others, like George Stevenson, would develop and **10)** _____ .

Score [ ] Percentage [%]

Cloze Test 4

Select the correct words to complete the passage below.

A GPO postal worker, named Patrick McKenna, and known by the 1)
- [ ] nickname
- [ ] title
- [ ] question

of *The Ulsterman*, had 2)
- [ ] fortune
- [ ] surprise
- [ ] knowledge

of the large amounts of bank notes being

3)
- [ ] amassed
- [ ] printed
- [ ] carried

by British Rail trains. He passed that information to Gordon Goody

and Buster Reynolds, who planned the Great Train Robbery of 1963. Their

4)
- [ ] boisterous
- [ ] criminal
- [ ] female

gang had no 5)
- [ ] competence
- [ ] trouble
- [ ] experience

of stopping and robbing trains,

so they 6)
- [ ] entitled
- [ ] enacted
- [ ] enlisted

the help of *The South Coast Raiders*, which included a

specialist in 7)
- [ ] rigging
- [ ] washing
- [ ] combing

trackside signals. In the early hours of 7th August, the

gang stopped and robbed the post office train 8)
- [ ] travailing
- [ ] travelling
- [ ] trundling

from Glasgow to

Euston, which contained 72 post office staff that 9)
- [ ] posted
- [ ] painted
- [ ] sorted

the mail during the

journey. They 10)
- [ ] stole
- [ ] printed
- [ ] withdrew

bank notes to the value of between £2.5 and £3

million pounds.

Score [ ]   Percentage [ ] %

Cloze Test 5

Fill in the missing letters to complete the passage below.

Construction of two **1)** | p | r | | t | o | t | | p | e | | of the turbojet-

powered supersonic passenger airliner began in February 1965: 001, built by

Aerospatiale at Toulouse, and 002, by BAC at Filton, Bristol. It was named *Concorde*

to reflect the Anglo-French **2)** | t | | e | | t | | which led to its development

and construction. The name *Concorde* is from the French word 'concorde', which has

an English **3)** | e | q | | i | v | | l | | n | t | , 'concord'. Both words mean

agreement, harmony or union. At the time *Concorde* was developed, the world was a

different place with hopes and **4)** | | s | p | i | | a | t | i | o | | s | that

5) | t | e | | | n | o | l | | g | i | | a | l | advances would change the

world we live in. On the afternoon of 2nd March 1969, *Concorde* 001 prepared to take

off on its **6)** | | a | i | d | e | | flight from the runway at Toulouse. The beautiful

'great white dart', flying at **7)** | | u | | e | r | s | o | | i | | speed, would

reduce the journey time from London to New York to three and a half hours instead of

eight. It would bring continents and **8)** | m | | n | | i | n | d | closer together.

Concorde 001 had been forced to wait on the ground for several days due to

9) | i | | c | l | e | m | | n | t | weather. At the controls was the French test

pilot, Andre Turcat, with co-pilot, Jacques Guignard, beside him in the cockpit. Also in

the aircraft were two engineers, while the British test pilot, Brian Trubshaw,

10) | | b | s | e | r | | e | | from the ground. *Concorde* was loaded with about ten tons of **11)** | i | | s | t | r | u | | e | n | t | a | | i | o | | to

record every aspect of the flight, and two chase aircraft would accompany the flight to

independently verify the speeds and film the flight from close by. At 15.40hrs *Concorde*

12) | t | h | | n | d | e | | e | | down the runway for almost a mile before

lifting its long, drooping, dart-like nose, and taking off for the first time. The hoards of

journalists and news crews burst into **13)** | s | | o | n | t | a | n | | | u | s |

applause as the four Rolls Royce *Olympus* jet engines thrust the magnificent and

graceful double delta-shaped winged aircraft into the sky. The flight, as planned, was

kept simple; neither the droop nose, designed for better

14) | v | i | | i | | i | l | | t | y | when landing, nor the landing gear was

raised during the 27 minute flight. Test pilot Trubshaw flew the aircraft

15) | | a | n | | a | l | | y | for the duration of the flight, taking *Concorde* to a

speed of only 300mph. The first airborne journey passed

16) | u | | e | v | | n | t | | u | l | l | | , unlike the second, from British

soil, when Brian Trubshaw had to land the aircraft with both altimeters

17) | i | | o | p | | r | a | t | | v | e | . *Concorde* first flew supersonic,

exceeding the speed of Mach 1, on its 45th flight in October 1969. *Concorde* was in

service with four carriers: Air France, British Airways, Braniff International Airways

and Singapore Airlines. It was finally **18)** | w | i | | h | d | | a | | n | in 2003.

Although it was never a commercial success, *Concorde* proved to be a

19) | | a | g | n | i | f | i | | e | n | | symbol of engineering

20) | g | e | n | | | s | .   **Score** | | | **Percentage** | | **%**

Cloze Test 6

Select the correct words to complete the passage below.

The discovery that there were oil **1)**
- ☐ mines
- ☐ tanks
- ☐ reserves

under the North Sea justified

British Petroleum's belief that their **2)**
- ☐ curiosity
- ☐ prospecting
- ☐ reports

would reap rewards. Until

the discovery, Britain **3)**
- ☐ relied
- ☐ stood
- ☐ existed

wholly on importing OPEC's oil from countries

in Africa, The Middle East and South America to satisfy the country's daily

4)
- ☐ ration
- ☐ delivery
- ☐ consumption

of two million barrels. On 3rd November 1975, the Queen

pushed the red button to **5)**
- ☐ commence
- ☐ holt
- ☐ overcome

the pumping ashore and production of

North Sea Oil. The Forties oilfield **6)**
- ☐ wasted
- ☐ signed
- ☐ provided

up to a quarter of Britain's oil

consumption and taxation revenue **7)**
- ☐ swelled
- ☐ reduce
- ☐ broke

the exchequer's

8)
- ☐ building
- ☐ head
- ☐ coffers

. It is estimated that around 76% of the North Sea oil reserves has

already been **9)**
- ☐ spent
- ☐ extracted
- ☐ created

so the oil bonanza may be coming to a

10)
- ☐ conclusion
- ☐ record
- ☐ summit

.

Score ☐ Percentage ☐ %

Cloze Test 7

Choose the correct words from the word bank below to complete the passage.

baby	worried	blunders	rode	crown
churches	cats	world	courted	buttercups

If the butterfly **1)** _____ the bee,

And the owl the porcupine;

If **2)** _____ were built in the sea,

And three times one was nine;

If the pony **3)** _____ his master,

If the **4)** _____ ate the cows,

If the **5)** _____ had the dire disaster

To be **6)** _____ , sir, by the mouse;

If mamma, sir, sold the **7)** _____

To a gypsy for half a **8)** _____ ;

If a gentleman, sir, was a lady, —

The **9)** _____ would be Upside-down!

If any or all of these wonders

Should ever come about,

I should not consider them **10)** _____ ,

For I should be inside-out!

Topsy-Turvy World by William Brighty Rands (1823-1882).

Score [ ] Percentage [ ] %

Cloze Test 8

Fill in the missing letters to complete the passage below.

There was, in fact, no part of his duty that the Reverend Mr. Mordaunt found so

decidedly **1)** | u | | p | | e | a | | a | n | t | as that part which compelled

him to call upon his noble patron at the Castle. His noble patron, indeed, usually

made these visits as **2)** | | i | s | a | g | | e | e | a | | l | e | as it lay in

his lordly power to make them. He **3)** | a | b | h | | r | r | | d | churches and

charities, and flew into violent rages when any of his tenantry took the

4) | l | i | | e | r | t | | of being poor and ill and needing assistance. When

his gout was at its worst, he did not **5)** | h | | s | i | t | | t | | to announce

that he would not be bored and **6)** | | r | r | i | t | | t | e | | by being told

stories of their miserable misfortunes; when his gout troubled him less and he was in

a somewhat more **7)** | h | u | | a | n | | frame of mind, he would perhaps give

the rector some money, after having bullied him in the most painful manner, and

8) | b | | r | a | t | | | the whole parish for its shiftlessness and imbecility.

But, whatsoever his mood, he never failed to make as many

9) | s | a | | c | a | s | | i | c | and embarrassing speeches as possible,

and to cause the Reverend Mr. Mordaunt to wish it were proper and Christian-like

to throw something heavy at him. During all the years in which Mr. Mordaunt had

been in charge of Dorincourt parish, the **10)** | r | | c | t | | r | certainly did

not remember having seen his lordship, of his own free will, do any one a kindness, or, under any **11)** `c` `_` `r` `c` `u` `_` `s` `t` `_` `n` `_` `e` `s` whatever,

show that he thought of any one but himself. He had called to-day to speak to him of

a specially **12)** `p` `_` `e` `s` `_` `i` `n` `_` case, and as he had walked up the

avenue, he had, for two reasons, **13)** `d` `r` `e` `_` `d` `e` `_` his visit more than

usual. In the first place, he knew that his lordship had for several days been suffering

with the gout, and had been in so **14)** `v` `i` `_` `l` `a` `_` `n` `o` `_` `s` a

humour that rumours of it had even reached the village—carried there by one of the

young women servants, to her sister, who kept a little shop and

15) `r` `_` `t` `_` `i` `l` `e` `d` darning-needles and cotton and peppermints

and gossip, as a means of earning an **16)** `_` `o` `n` `e` `_` `t` living. What Mrs.

Dibble did not know about the Castle and its inmates, and the farm-houses and their

inmates, and the **17)** `v` `i` `l` `l` `_` `_` `_` and its population, was really

not worth being talked about. And of course she knew everything about the Castle,

because her sister, Jane Shorts, was one of the upper housemaids, and was very

friendly and **18)** `i` `_` `t` `i` `m` `_` `t` `_` with Thomas.

"And the way his lordship do go on!" said Mrs. Dibble, over the counter, "and the

way he do use **19)** `l` `_` `n` `g` `_` `a` `g` `_` , Mr. Thomas told Jane herself, no

flesh and blood as is in livery could stand—for throw a plate of toast at Mr. Thomas,

hisself, he did, not more than two days since, and if it weren't for other things being

20) `_` `g` `r` `_` `e` `a` `_` `l` `e` and the society below stairs most genteel,

warning would have been gave within a' hour!"

Extract from *Little Lord Fauntleroy*
by Frances Hodgson Burnett (1849-1924).

Score [ ] **Percentage** [ ] **%**

ae © 2015 Stephen Curran

Cloze Test 9

Choose the correct words from the word bank below to complete the passage.

pursue	complained	trial	patented	immunising
popularly	mauled	sour	growth	discoveries

Louis Pasteur (1822-1895) was a French chemist and microbiologist who is renowned for his **1)** _____ of the principles of microbial fermentation, pasteurisation and vaccination.

In 1856, he was approached by a local manufacturer of wine who **2)** _____ that, when making beetroot alcohol, the wine would **3)** _____ after a short while in storage. Pasteur's research into fermentation showed that the **4)** _____ of micro-organisms was responsible for spoiling beverages, such as beer, wine and milk. By heating liquids to a temperature of between 60 and 100°C, he discovered that most bacteria were killed. He **5)** _____ the process and the method became known as Pasteurisation.

This knowledge led him to **6)** _____ the notion that micro-organisms caused infection in animals and humans. He began looking at the cause of chicken cholera and developed a vaccine which, by **7)** _____ them against it, prevented infection. Vaccines against anthrax in cattle and rabies in dogs followed. The first human **8)** _____ took place in 1885 on a nine year old boy who had been **9)** _____ by a rabid dog. The boy showed no sign of infection and Pasteur was hailed as a hero.

He is **10)** _____ known as the "father of microbiology".

Score ☐ Percentage ☐ %

Cloze Test 10

Select the correct words to complete the passage below.

To prevent the spread of infectious 1) ☐ diseases ☐ noises ☐ spores , the chain of infection needs to be

broken by a process known as hygiene. Most hygiene practices were 2) ☐ rejected ☐ divulged ☐ developed

in the 19th century and were well 3) ☐ established ☐ forgotten ☐ patented by the mid-20th century. They

are practised in the home, hospitals, food processing plants and animal

4) ☐ happiness ☐ bones ☐ husbandry . Simple routines, such as washing hands 5) ☐ gingerly ☐ thoroughly ☐ quickly

before preparing or eating food, or between examining patients in hospital, are

6) ☐ sufficient ☐ avoided ☐ unlikely to prevent the spread of viruses. This simple precaution removes

infectious 7) ☐ odours ☐ fumes ☐ microbes as well as dirt and grime. Keeping all work surfaces and

kitchen 8) ☐ utilities ☐ utensils ☐ utilises clean to prevent cross-contamination, and 9) ☐ sterilising ☐ cooling ☐ sharpening

surgical instruments in hospital theatres minimises the risk of infection from the

spreading of 10) ☐ germs ☐ gels ☐ saliva .

Score ☐ Percentage ☐ %

Cloze Test 11

Fill in the missing letters to complete the passage below.

In the 20th century, demand for electricity led to the

1) c | | n | s | | d | e | r | | t | i | | n | of geothermal power as a

generating source. The world's oldest geothermal district heating system in Chaudes-

Aigues, France, has been operating since the 14th century. The first geothermal power

2) g | | n | e | | a | | o | r | was tested by Prince Piero Ginori Conti in

1904, at the Larderello dry steam field where geothermal acid

3) | x | t | r | a | | t | i | | n | began. The generator successfully lit four

light bulbs. Later, in 1911, the world's first **4)** c | o | | m | e | | c | i | | l

geothermal power plant was built there. It was the world's only industrial producer of

geothermal electricity until New Zealand built a **5)** | | l | a | n | | in 1958. The

heat pump, used to draw heat from the ground, was **6)** i | n | | e | n | t | e |

by Lord Kelvin in 1852 and, in 1912, a patent for the idea was

7) g | | a | n | t | | d | to Heinrich Zoelly, However, it was not until the late

1940s that the geothermal heat pump was successfully

8) i | m | p | | e | m | e | | t | e | | . Geothermal energy is heat

9) d | r | a | | | from the earth, which is used as an affordable and

10) s | | s | t | a | | n | a | | l | e | solution to reducing dependence on

fossil fuels. In the United States, more than 40 geothermal plants, which account for

80% of the nation's **11)** c | a | | a | c | | t | y | , are located in California and provide nearly 7% of the state's electricity. Heat pumps

12) | u | | i | l | i | | e | the steady temperatures found just underground to

provide heating and cooling for thousands of buildings across the United States. In

Iceland, the world leader in direct applications, over 90% of its homes are

13) | | e | a | t | | d | with geothermal energy, saving Iceland over $100

million annually in avoided oil **14)** | i | | p | o | | t | s | . Reykjavík has the

world's biggest district heating system and, while it was once the most

15) | p | | | l | u | t | | d | city in the world, it is now one of the cleanest.

It confirms that geothermal energy is a source of clean and inexpensive power. To

explain geothermal energy and how it is generated, it is necessary to look beneath

the Earth's surface. Below the **16)** | c | | u | s | | , there is a layer of hot and

molten rock, called magma, in which **17)** | d | | c | a | y | | g | natural

radioactive materials, such as uranium and potassium, are a continual source of heat

production. The difference in temperature between the core of the planet and its

surface, known as the geothermal gradient, drives a continuous

18) | c | | n | d | | c | t | i | | n | of thermal energy in the form of heat

from the core to the surface. At a depth of 10,000 metres below the surface of the

Earth, the amount of heat contains 50,000 times more energy than all the oil and

19) | | a | t | u | r | | l | gas resources in the world. The areas where the

highest underground temperatures may be found are in regions with

20) | a | | t | i | | e | or geologically young volcanoes.

Score | | Percentage | | %

Cloze Test 12

Select the correct words to complete the passage below.

The elephant, thanks to the **1)**
- [ ] poor
- [ ] random
- [ ] skilful

guidance of the Parsee, was advancing

rapidly through the still darksome forest, and, an hour after leaving the pagoda, had

crossed a vast **2)**
- [ ] plain
- [ ] ocean
- [ ] hill

. They made a **3)**
- [ ] halt
- [ ] mistake
- [ ] rush

at seven o'clock, the

young woman being still in a state of complete **4)**
- [ ] excitement
- [ ] prostration
- [ ] darkness

. The guide made

her drink a little brandy and water, but the drowsiness which **5)**
- [ ] covered
- [ ] helped
- [ ] stupefied

her

could not yet be shaken off. Sir Francis, who was familiar with the **6)**
- [ ] benefits
- [ ] justice
- [ ] effects

of the intoxication produced by the **7)**
- [ ] fumes
- [ ] clouds
- [ ] streams

of hemp, reassured his

companions on her account. But he was more **8)**
- [ ] pleased
- [ ] disturbed
- [ ] stern

at the prospect of her

future **9)**
- [ ] wealth
- [ ] features
- [ ] fate

. He told Phileas Fogg that, should Aouda remain in India, she

would **10)**
- [ ] inevitably
- [ ] sometimes
- [ ] studiously

fall again into the hands of her executioners.

Extract from *Around the World in Eighty Days*
by Jules Verne (1828-1905).

Score ☐ Percentage ☐ %

Cloze Test 13

Choose the correct words from the word bank below to complete the passage.

capability	lethal	administered	fangs	sting
predator	inject	evolved	toxins	allergic

Many animals use venom to kill their prey. They may bite, **1)** _____ or use another part of their body to inject the deadly substance into their victim. The diet of venomous animals has also **2)** _____ to include the venomous substance without harming the **3)** _____ . The venom secreted by different animals is highly specialised and is specifically designed to deliver a **4)** _____ or paralysing dose to the particular quarry of each venomous animal. Although the main purpose of venomous **5)** _____ is to kill an animal's prey, some animals also to use it as a method of defence. The range of animals with a venomous **6)** _____ is wide: many snakes, invertebrates, fish, and reptiles have the ability to bite, sting or stab their victims to **7)** _____ the toxin. Snakes have **8)** _____ , as do spiders and some fish. Other animals, such as centipedes, scorpions, bees, wasps, and some fish, sting their victims. The reaction of humans to animal venom varies. Bee and wasp stings are seldom fatal, unless the victim suffers from a serious **9)** _____ reaction, called anaphylaxis. Snake and spider bites can be more serious but antivenoms are effective, provided they are **10)** _____ soon after.

Score [   ] Percentage [   ] %

Cloze Test 14

Fill in the missing letters to complete the passage.

As round their **1)** | d | | i | n | | father's bed

His sons attend, the **2)** | p | e | | s | a | | t | said:

"Children, deep hid from **3)** | p | | y | i | n | | eyes,

A **4)** | | r | e | a | s | | r | | in my vineyard lies;

When you have laid me in the **5)** | g | | r | | v | | ,

Dig, search—and your **6)** | r | | w | a | | d | you'll have."

"Father," cries one, "but where's the spot?"

He sighs! he **7)** | s | | | n | k | | ! he answers not.

The **8)** | t | e | | i | o | | s | burial service over,

Home go his sons, and **9)** | | t | r | a | i | | h | | explore

Each corner of the **10)** | v | | n | e | | a | r | d | round,

Dig up, beat, break, and **11)** | s | | f | t | the ground;

Yet though to search so well **12)** | i | n | c | | i | n | e | | ,

Nor gold, nor treasure could they find;

But when the **13)** | a | | t | u | | n | next drew near,

A double **14)** | v | | n | t | a | g | | crowned the year.

"Now," **15)** | q | | o | t | h | the peasant's wisest son,

"Our father's **16)** | l | | g | a | | y | is known,

In yon rich **17)** | | u | r | p | | e | grapes 'tis seen,

Which, but for **18)** | d | | g | g | i | | g | , never had been.

Then let us all **19)** | r | e | | l | e | c | | with pleasure.

That **20)** | l | | b | o | | r | is the source of treasure."

The Father's Treasure by Anon.

Score [ ] Percentage [ ] %

Cloze Test 15

Choose the correct words from the word bank below to complete the passage.

tubing	**topics**	**essential**	**projection**	**paramount**
structures	**derived**	**scanning**	**membrane**	**mechanical**

The word "acoustic" is **1)** _____ from the Greek word *akoustikos*,

meaning "of or for hearing, ready to hear". Acoustics is the study of all

2) _____ waves in liquids, gases and solids and includes

3) _____ such as sound, vibration, ultrasound and infrasound. The

science of acoustics covers many subjects including music, architecture, medicine,

the workplace, industrial production, and even warfare. Knowledge of acoustics is

4) _____ when designing musical instruments. How the strings on a

violin, the effect of the length of **5)** _____ in a brass instrument, and

the shape of a drum **6)** _____ affect the performance of an acoustic

instrument is of **7)** _____ importance to their design. The design, choice

of materials, and construction of a theatre or music hall must be sympathetic to

the quality and **8)** _____ of sound within the auditorium. In medicine,

acoustics are used in developing ultrasound **9)** _____ . Acoustic location

uses sound to determine the distance and direction of something. It may take place

in liquids, gases or solids, so may be used to measure the depth of the oceans,

the distance of objects in space, or to find objects or **10)** _____ deep

underground.

Score [　　] Percentage [　　] %

Cloze Test 16

Fill in the missing letters to complete the passage.

When I was sick and lay a-bed,

I had two **1)** | p | | l | l | | w | s | at my head,

And all my toys **2)** | b | e | | i | d | | me lay,

To keep me happy all the day.

And sometimes for an hour or so

I watched my leaden **3)** | s | | l | d | | e | r | | go,

With different **4)** | | n | i | f | | r | | s | and drills,

Among the bed-clothes, through the hills;

And **5)** | s | o | | e | t | | m | | s | sent my ships in fleets

All up and down among the sheets;

Or **6)** | b | | o | u | | h | | my trees and houses out,

And **7)** | | l | a | n | t | | d | cities all about.

I was the **8)** | g | | | n | t | great and still

That sits upon the pillow-hill,

And sees before him, **9)** | d | | l | e | and plain,

The pleasant land of **10)** | c | o | | n | t | | r | p | | n | e | .

The Land of Counterpane by Robert Louis Stevenson (1850-1894).

Score ☐ Percentage ☐ %

Cloze Test 17

Select the correct words to complete the passage below.

It happened one day, about noon, going 1) [ ] over / [ ] among / [ ] towards my boat, I was

2) [ ] hardly / [ ] exceedingly / [ ] awkwardly surprised with the print of a man's 3) [ ] naked / [ ] pink / [ ] gloved foot on the

shore, which was very plain to be seen on the 4) [ ] pebbles / [ ] rocks / [ ] sand . I stood like one

thunderstruck, or as if I had seen an 5) [ ] apparition / [ ] elephant / [ ] instant . I listened, I looked round

me, but I could hear nothing, nor see anything; I went up to a 6) [ ] rising / [ ] low / [ ] watery ground

to look farther; I went up the shore and down the shore, but it was all one; I could see

no other 7) [ ] seaweed / [ ] impression / [ ] ship but that one. I went to it again to see if there were any

more, and to 8) [ ] cope / [ ] struggle / [ ] observe if it might not be my fancy; but there was no room for

that, for there was 9) [ ] not / [ ] hidden / [ ] exactly the print of a foot—toes, heel, and every part of a

foot. How it came 10) [ ] thither / [ ] not / [ ] around I knew not, nor could I in the least imagine; but

after 11) [ ] colourful / [ ] innumerable / [ ] innovative fluttering thoughts, like a man perfectly

12)
- [ ] rich
- [ ] ill
- [ ] confused

and out of myself, I came home to my **13)**
- [ ] fortification
- [ ] sheltered
- [ ] classroom

, not

feeling, as we say, the ground I went on, but **14)**
- [ ] happy
- [ ] terrified
- [ ] ransomed

to the last degree,

looking behind me at every two or three steps, **15)**
- [ ] mistaking
- [ ] cutting
- [ ] hearing

every bush and

tree, and fancying every **16)**
- [ ] hill
- [ ] cave
- [ ] stump

at a distance to be a man. Nor is it possible

to **17)**
- [ ] conscript
- [ ] decant
- [ ] describe

how many various shapes my **18)**
- [ ] purple
- [ ] affrighted
- [ ] skeletal

imagination

represented things to me in, how many wild ideas were found every moment in my

19)
- [ ] fancy
- [ ] pocket
- [ ] throat

, and what strange, unaccountable **20)**
- [ ] tastes
- [ ] rushes
- [ ] whimsies

came into my

thoughts by the way.

Extract from *The Life and Adventures of Robinson Crusoe*
by Daniel Defoe (1660-1731).

Score [   ]   Percentage [   ] %

Cloze Test 18

Fill in the missing letters to complete the passage.

The Highway Code was first published on 14th April 1931, and priced at just one penny

and **1)** [| o | n | t | a | | n | e |] only 18 pages of advice. It was produced

in response to the **2)** [d | i | | t | u | r | | i | n | | l |] high death rate

on Britain's roads. Although there were only 2.3 million vehicles on Britain's roads

at the time, the lack of a **3)** [c | o | m | | u | | s | o | | y] driving test

contributed to the 7,000 deaths each year. The first edition urged road users to be careful

and **4)** [| o | n | s | | d | e | | a | t | e] to others and to put safety first. An

expanded, more complete version was published in 1934. It included information on road

signs and the dangers of driving under the **5)** [i | n | | l | | e | n | | e] of

alcohol. A further revised edition included advice on how to join and leave a motorway,

the danger of **6)** [| i | r | e | | n | e | | s] , and the need for drivers to use

the service areas to rest and to **7)** [s | t | | e | | | h] their legs. The 1978

edition added the Green Cross Code and advice on improved vehicle

8) [s | | c | u | | i | | y] was included. The Highway Code applies to

animals, pedestrians, cyclists, motorcyclists, and drivers, and failure to comply with

the **9)** [m | | n | d | | t | | r | y] rules is a criminal offence. Significantly,

although the number of vehicles on Britain's roads has increased to over 30 million, the

number of road deaths has fallen to around 2,000

10) [a | | n | u | a | | l] .   Score [   ]   Percentage [   ] %

Cloze Test 19

Select the correct words to complete the passage below.

James Blundell, born in London in 1791, was an English obstetrician

1)
- ☐ renowned
- ☐ recalled
- ☐ repealed

for performing the first successful **2)**
- ☐ transcript
- ☐ transformation
- ☐ transfusion

of

human blood to a patient for **3)**
- ☐ treatment
- ☐ blockage
- ☐ prevention

of a haemorrhage. He had

4)
- ☐ advised
- ☐ charged
- ☐ witnessed

many of his patients dying in childbirth and **5)**
- ☐ chose
- ☐ prayed
- ☐ resolved

to

find a remedy. Blundell conducted experiments with animal blood transfusions using

a **6)**
- ☐ syringe
- ☐ cylinder
- ☐ funnel

. He also discovered that he could collect the blood from the

7)
- ☐ recipient
- ☐ corpse
- ☐ donor

in a container before transfusing it into the **8)**
- ☐ recipient
- ☐ donor
- ☐ receptacle

.

In 1829, Dr Blundell **9)**
- ☐ accepted
- ☐ accomplished
- ☐ aquired

the first blood transfusion between two

humans. During his life he also **10)**
- ☐ destroyed
- ☐ divulged
- ☐ devised

many instruments for the

transfusion of blood, many of which are still in use today.

Score ☐ Percentage ☐ %

Cloze Test 20

Choose the correct words from the word bank below to complete the passage.

stomach	villainous	acted	speculated	perpetrated
theories	inexplicably	stuffed	faked	confiscated
revenue	apprehended	knack	embarrass	befriended
violent	accomplices	exhumed	granted	Roundhead

On 9th May 1671, an infamous crime was **1)** _____ by the self-styled Colonel Thomas Blood. During the Civil War, this Irishman switched allegiances from Royalist to **2)** _____ and became a Parliamentary supporter. During the war, he **3)** _____ as a spy for Cromwell's army. Blood was given estates in Ireland for his services but they were **4)** _____ when Charles II was restored to the throne. He was involved in many **5)** _____ adventures, including attempted kidnap and working with dissident religious movements. The Colonel had the **6)** _____ of disappearing and evading capture by government forces. In 1671, Blood attempted to steal the Crown Jewels from the Tower of London. Over several days, pretending to be a parson, he

7) _____ the King's Jewel Keeper, Talbot Edwards, with an offer for his fictitious nephew to marry Edwards' daughter, and thereby secure a sizable income. Later, he tricked Edwards into letting Blood and his two **8)** _____ into the jewel room. Once inside, the jewel keeper was hit on the head with a mallet and, when he continued to struggle, he was bound, gagged and stabbed in the

9) _____ . Blood used the mallet to flatten St. Edwards Crown and hid it under his clerical cloak while his accomplice, Blood's brother-in-law Hunt, filed the Sceptre with the Cross in two (as it did not fit in their bag), while the third man, Parrot, **10)** _____ the Sovereign's Orb down his trousers. The robbers were disturbed and tried to flee, but they were all **11)** _____ . Blood

refused to be questioned by anyone and demanded to speak to the King himself.

12) _____ , his request was granted and he was interviewed in private by

the monarch. Although a wanted man with a price on his head for previous

13) _____ crimes, mysteriously, Blood was released after a short time.

Furthermore, he was **14)** _____ a royal free pardon, awarded an annual

pension of £500, and his confiscated Irish estates were returned to him. It has been

15) _____ that Blood may have been working for the King, stealing the

Crown Jewels to provide much needed **16)** _____ for Charles II. Other

17) _____ are that he was being repaid for his spying, or that he knew

things that could **18)** _____ the crown. Blood died at his home in 1680

and was buried in the churchyard of St Margaret's Church near St. James's Park. It is

believed that his body was **19)** _____ by the authorities for confirmation:

such was his reputation for trickery, it was suspected he might have

20) _____ his death and funeral.

Score [ ] **Percentage** [ ] **%**

Cloze Test 21

Fill in the missing letters to complete the passage below.

At 9.18am on 22nd April 1884 an earthquake, which became known as the

Colchester earthquake or the Great English Earthquake, shook South East England.

Its **1)** `e _ i c _ n t _ e` was the villages of Wivenhoe, Abberton,

Langenhoe and Peldon. It measured 4.6 on the Richter scale, lasted for about 20

seconds, and the tremors were felt across England, and even in France and Belgium.

The earthquake has been **2)** `a _ t r i b _ t e _` with claiming 3

to 5 lives, although contemporary accounts dispute this. The Times reported damage

"in the many villages in the **3)** `n e _ g _ b o _ r h _ o d`

of Colchester", and, according to local newspapers, almost every building had

been affected. The Masonry **4)** `t _ m b _ e d` off the tower of the

medieval church in Langenhoe, crashing into the roof of the nave and chancel. The

nearby rectory was also damaged. Many poor people were made homeless and a

5) `_ o n s i _ e r _ b l _` number of small craft were

destroyed by the waves created by the seismic **6)** `a _ t i _ i t _`.

Earthquakes are a rarity in England and the

7) `i n _ a b i _ a n t _` living in and around Colchester were

terrified by the **8)** `f _ e r _ _ i t _` of the earthquake. The cause of

the earthquake is thought to have been a movement along a **9)** `f a _ l _` in

the ancient Palaeozoic rocks that **10)** `u _ d _ r p _ n` most of Essex.

Score ☐ Percentage ☐ %

Cloze Test 22

Select the correct words to complete the passage below.

The Order of Companion of Honour may be **1)**
- ☐ bestowed
- ☐ piled
- ☐ ladeled

upon persons who

have given **2)**
- ☐ reduced
- ☐ conspicuous
- ☐ speedy

national service and for whom the **3)**
- ☐ distinction
- ☐ road
- ☐ juncture

is deemed to be the most **4)**
- ☐ expensive
- ☐ useless
- ☐ appropriate

form of recognition. The Order was

instituted in 1917 by King George V, in the same year as the **5)**
- ☐ future
- ☐ failures
- ☐ founding

of the

British Empire. At any time, the Order comprises the **6)**
- ☐ Sovereign
- ☐ Minister
- ☐ Headmaster

and only 65

members, although foreigners may be admitted as honorary Companions.

7)
- ☐ Recipients
- ☐ Rascals
- ☐ Renegades

are entitled to add 'CH' after their name. The Order's badge is a

gold, oval-shaped **8)**
- ☐ certificate
- ☐ ribbon
- ☐ medallion

with a representation of an oak tree. Its

9)
- ☐ function
- ☐ price
- ☐ motto

is "In action faithful and in honour clear." Recipients include artists,

scientists, actors, poets, historians, **10)**
- ☐ politicians
- ☐ plumbers
- ☐ publicans

and musicians.

Score ☐ Percentage ☐ %

Cloze Test 23

Choose the correct words from the word bank below to complete the passage.

woody	**whitewashed**	**darkness**	**may**	**jockey**
cast	**disbeliever**	**trunks**	**clap**	**shaded**
bolted	**haunt**	**galloped**	**overtaken**	**beaming**
sunbeams	**encountered**	**foray**	**punch**	**turned**

The sequestered situation of this church seems always to have made it a favourite

1) _____ of troubled spirits. It stands on a knoll, surrounded by locust-

trees and lofty elms, from among which its decent, **2)** _____ walls shine

modestly forth, like Christian purity **3)** _____ through the shades of

retirement. A gentle slope descends from it to a silver sheet of water, bordered by

high trees, between which, peeps **4)** _____ be caught at the blue hills of

the Hudson. To look upon its grass-grown yard, where the **5)** _____ seem

to sleep so quietly, one would think that there at least the dead might rest in peace. On

one side of the church extends a wide **6)** _____ dell, along which raves

a large brook among broken rocks and **7)** _____ of fallen trees. Over a

deep black part of the stream, not far from the church, was formerly thrown a wooden

bridge; the road that led to it, and the bridge itself, were thickly **8)** _____

by overhanging trees, which **9)** _____ a gloom about it, even in the

daytime; but occasioned a fearful **10)** _____ at night. Such was one of

the favourite haunts of the Headless Horseman, and the place where he was most

frequently **11)** _____ . The tale was told of old Brouwer, a most heretical

12) _____ in ghosts, how he met the Horseman returning from his

13) _____ into Sleepy Hollow, and was obliged to get up behind him;

how they **14)** _____ over bush and brake, over hill and swamp, until they reached the bridge; when the Horseman suddenly **15)** _____ into a skeleton, threw old Brouwer into the brook, and sprang away over the tree-tops with a **16)** _____ of thunder.

This story was immediately matched by a thrice marvellous adventure of Brom Bones, who made light of the Galloping Hessian as an arrant **17)** _____ . He affirmed that on returning one night from the neighbouring village of Sing Sing, he had been **18)** _____ by this midnight trooper; that he had offered to race with him for a bowl of **19)** _____ , and should have won it too, for Daredevil beat the goblin horse all hollow, but just as they came to the church bridge, the Hessian **20)** _____ , and vanished in a flash of fire.

Extract from *The Legend of Sleepy Hollow* by Washington Irvine (1783-1859).

Score ☐ Percentage ☐ %

Cloze Test 24

Fill in the missing letters to complete the passage below.

On 21st October 1966, in the small mining village of Aberfan, South Wales, a most

1) | h | | r | r | | w | | n | g | disaster occurred that took the lives of 116

children and 28 adults. At 9.15am, the children of Pantglas Junior School were

returning to their classrooms after morning assembly. After several days of heavy

rain, a build-up of rainwater in the **2)** | a | c | c | | m | u | | a | t | | d |

rock and shale caused the colliery waste tip to suddenly slide downhill in an

3) | | v | a | l | a | | c | h | | of slurry. Over 150,000 cubic metres of

4) | d | e | b | | | s | covered the village in minutes,

5) | e | n | | u | l | | i | n | | the school and 20 houses. At the time, the

village, **6)** | | e | s | t | l | | | g | in the valley, was

7) | s | | r | o | | d | e | | in fog. The sound of the impending disaster could

be heard as the enormous volume of earth and coal waste thundered towards the

village. Almost 2,000 volunteers rushed to the scene in a **8)** | | r | a | | t | | c |

rescue operation, but they were powerless to prevent the tragic loss of life. In 1958,

the tip had been sited on a known stream and had previously suffered several minor

slips. Its **9)** | | n | s | t | a | | i | l | | t | y | was known both to colliery

management and to tip workers, but very little was done about it. The National

Coal Board was heavily **10)** | c | | i | t | i | | i | s | e | | in the

ensuing tribunal.

Score [   ] Percentage [   ] %

Cloze Test 25

Select the correct words to complete the passage below.

Contrary to public **1)**
☐ misconception
☐ footpaths
☐ fascination
, Henry Ford (1863-1947) invented neither

the motor car nor the assembly line. He did, however, manufacture the first

2)
☐ wheeled
☐ green
☐ affordable
motor car, the Model T, and make it a practical

3)
☐ conveyance
☐ joke
☐ solution
. He is credited with introducing a moving **4)**
☐ washing
☐ assembly
☐ white
line

that enabled a relatively unskilled worker to learn a simple, **5)**
☐ repetitive
☐ difficult
☐ expensive

operation. Ford was a philanthropist, who was **6)**
☐ reluctant
☐ destined
☐ eager
to ensure his

employees were **7)**
☐ poorly
☐ never
☐ adequately
rewarded with high wages. He became one of the

richest people in the world and left most of his wealth to the Ford Foundation that is

8)
☐ committed
☐ beckoned
☐ welded
to programmes that strengthen **9)**
☐ low
☐ property
☐ democratic
values, reduce

poverty and **10)**
☐ temperatures
☐ criticism
☐ injustice
, and advance human knowledge, creativity and

achievement.

Score ☐ Percentage ☐ %

Cloze Test 26

Choose the correct words from the word bank below to complete the passage.

suffix	**increased**	**plaques**	**respectively**	**revolutionary**
tension	**portrayed**	**identical**	**proportions**	**constitutes**
evolved	**popular**	**debatable**	**superseded**	**obviated**
sharply	**resembles**	**gradually**	**counterparts**	**construction**

The oldest iconic representation of a stringed instrument is **1)** _____ in a stone carving which is more than 3,300 years old. An instrument that bears a strong resemblance to a guitar is illustrated in Babylonian clay **2)** _____ , so it may be that the origin of the guitar predates 12th Century chordophones. There are five basic types of chordophones, which were developed across Europe: bows, harps, lutes, lyres, and zithers, of which the lute most closely **3)** _____ a guitar. One of the earliest of these is a long-necked lute, either Roman or Byzantine, from Egypt. The lute has a waisted soundbox (or body) like a guitar and was **4)** _____ from the third to sixth century. The vihuela, which dates from the 14th to the 17th century, is larger than a guitar, has six or seven doubled strings (paired courses) and is tuned like a lute. Some illustrations show it with a **5)** _____ cut waist, similar to a violin, while others show rounded corners more like a guitar. Both the vihuela and the guitar coexisted until the 17th century, when the guitar's popularity **6)** _____ that of the vihuela. The last surviving music for the vihuela was published in 1576. The definition of exactly what **7)** _____ a guitar is given as having "a long, fretted neck, flat wooden soundboard, ribs, and a flat back, most often with incurved sides". The modern English word "guitar" and its French and German **8)** _____ , "guitare" and "Gitarre" **9)** _____ , are derived from the Spanish "guitarra". This word comes from the Andalusian Arabic "quitara". The

10) _____ , "tar" is the ancient Sanskrit word for "string". The prefix

denotes the number of strings: *dotar* – two strings; *setar* – three strings; *chartar* –

four strings. The four-course "chitarra" was **11)** _____ replaced by the

five-course "guitarra battente", which had a standard tuning **12)** _____

to the top five strings of a modern-day guitar. Over time, the neck length from the

instrument's body was **13)** _____ from 8 frets to 10 frets, then to 12

frets. In the 17th century, the Italians added a sixth course of strings, which finally

14) _____ into six single strings. In 1850, the Spanish luthier, Antonio

Torres, redesigned the guitar and introduced the **15)** _____ "fan- top"

bracing pattern. To improve the volume, tone and projection of the instrument, the

size and **16)** _____ of the body were altered. The classical guitar has

since remained essentially unchanged to this day. Around 1900, the advent of steel

strings presented the opportunity to build louder guitars. However, the fan-braced top

of classical guitars was not capable of withstanding the increased

17) _____ of steel strings. X-braced tops, first developed by a German

immigrant to the USA, Christian Fredrich Martin, became the industry standard for

the **18)** _____ of steel strung flat-top guitars. In the late 1920s, with the

advent of amplification, pick-ups were added to jazz guitars. This

19) _____ the need for a hollow body, giving rise to the construction of

solid body electric guitars. The creator of the first solid bodied guitar is

20) _____ but, from its humble beginnings, the guitar has evolved into

one of the most popular instruments of choice.

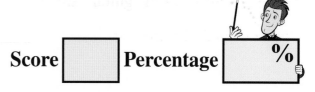

Score [ ] Percentage [ ] %

Cloze Test 27

Select the correct words to complete the passage below.

She lingered, and resisted my **1)**
- [ ] persuasions
- [ ] sights
- [ ] persuant

to departure a tiresome while; but

as he neither looked up nor spoke, she finally made a **2)**
- [ ] shout
- [ ] handle
- [ ] movement

to the door,

and I followed. We were recalled by a **3)**
- [ ] scream
- [ ] cloud
- [ ] soldier

. Linton had slid from his seat

on to the hearthstone, and lay **4)**
- [ ] comfortably
- [ ] crawling
- [ ] writhing

in the mere perverseness of an

indulged plague of a child, determined to be as **5)**
- [ ] grievous
- [ ] still
- [ ] conscious

and harassing as it

can. I thoroughly **6)**
- [ ] smelled
- [ ] stunned
- [ ] gauged

his disposition from his behaviour, and saw at once

it would be **7)**
- [ ] stutter
- [ ] rich
- [ ] folly

to attempt humouring him. Not so my

8)
- [ ] companion
- [ ] brother
- [ ] horse

: she ran back in terror, **9)**
- [ ] rolled
- [ ] stood
- [ ] knelt

down, and cried, and

soothed, and entreated, till he grew quiet from lack of **10)**
- [ ] breath
- [ ] food
- [ ] fears

: by no means

from compunction at distressing her.

Extract from *Wuthering Heights* by Emily Brontë (1818-1848).

Score ☐ Percentage ☐ %

© 2015 Stephen Curran

Cloze Test 28

Fill in the missing letters to complete the passage below.

Standing only 4ft 10in, the diminutive Helena Rubinstein was born in 1884. When

she **1)** | e | m | | g | r | | t | | d | from her native Poland to Australia in

1902 she had no money and little English. However, her

2) | s | t | | l | i | | | clothes and milky-white

3) | c | | m | p | l | e | | i | o | | did not go unnoticed and she found a

ready market for the jars of beauty cream in her luggage. She decided to

4) | | a | n | u | | a | c | t | u | | e | her own, using lanolin extracted from

sheep's wool with essence of lavender, pine bark or water lilies added to disguise

the **5)** | p | | n | g | | n | t | odour. She was "the first self-made female

millionaire", an **6)** | a | c | | o | m | | l | i | | h | | e | n | t | she owed

primarily to publicity savvy. She knew how to advertise—using 'fear copy with a bit

of blah-blah'—and introduced the **7)** | c | | n | | e | p | | of 'problem' skin

types. She also pioneered the use of pseudoscience in marketing,

8) | d | | n | n | i | | g | a lab coat in many advertisements, despite the fact

that her only training had been a two-month tour of European skin-care facilities. She

knew how to manipulate consumers' status anxiety, as well: If a product

9) | f | | l | t | | r | e | | initially, she would hike the price to raise the

10) | p | e | | c | e | i | v | | d | value. She died a multi-millionaire in 1965.

Score [ ] **Percentage** [ ] **%**

Cloze Test 29

Choose the correct words from the word bank below to complete the passage.

giggles	**gentleman**	**rude**	**terrible**	**matters**
bade	**disgrace**	**tilts**	**dinner**	**fidgety**
snapped	**cloth**	**able**	**bare**	**tumbling**
fret	**grave**	**fairly**	**swings**	**child**

'Let me see if Philip can

Be a little **1)** _____ ;

Let me see if he is **2)** _____

To sit still for once at table:'

Thus Papa **3)** _____ Phil behave;

And Mamma looked very **4)** _____ .

But **5)** _____ Phil,

He won't sit still;

He wriggles,

And **6)** _____ ,

And then, I declare,

7) _____ backwards and forwards,

And **8)** _____ up his chair,

Just like any rocking-horse

'Philip! I am getting cross!'

See the naughty, restless **9)** _____

Growing still more **10)** _____ and wild,

Till his chair falls over quite.

Philip screams with all his might,

Catches at the **11)** _____ , but then

That makes **12)** _____ worse again.

Down upon the ground they fall,

Glasses, plates, knives, forks, and all.

How Mamma did **13)** _____ and frown,

When she saw them **14)** _____ down!

And Papa made such a face!

Philip is in sad **15)** _____ .

Where is Philip, where is he?

16) _____ covered up you see!

Cloth and all are lying on him;

He has pulled down all upon him.

What a **17)** _____ to-do!

Dishes, glasses, **18)** _____ in two!

Here a knife, and there a fork!

Philip, this is cruel work.

Table all so **19)** _____ , and ah!

Poor Papa, and poor Mamma

Look quite cross, and wonder how

They shall have their **20)** _____ now.

The Story of Fidgety Philip
by Heinrich Hoffmann (1809-1894).

Score [ ] **Percentage** [%]

Cloze Test 30

Fill in the missing letters to complete the passage below.

María Eva Duarte de Perón was born in 1919 in **1)** [r][ ][r][ ][l] Argentina.

She is usually referred to as Eva Perón, or by the affectionate Spanish language

2) [d][i][ ][i][n][ ][t][i][ ][e], Evita. At the age of 15, she moved

to Buenos Aires to pursue a career on the stage and radio, but she had to survive

without **3)** [ ][o][r][m][ ][l] education or connections. Eventually, she was

4) [c][ ][n][t][ ][a][c][ ][e][d] to the biggest radio station, and by 1943

she was one of the highest paid radio actresses in Argentina. Her success gave her

sufficient financial **5)** [s][ ][a][b][ ][l][i][ ][ ][y] to enable her to move into

her own apartment in the most exclusive area of Buenos Aires. Eva Duarte's husband,

Juan Perón, was Minister of Labour and had

6) [c][o][ ][s][i][ ][e][r][ ][b][l][ ] support from the army and the

country. Perón was arrested and imprisoned by his opponents in the government but

was released six days later as a result of public

7) [ ][e][ ][o][n][ ][t][ ][a][t][ ][o][n][s]. When he stood for

president, in 1946, Eva delivered powerful speeches in his support on her radio

show and he won a **8)** [l][a][ ][d][s][ ][i][d][ ] victory. In 1947,

unaccompanied by her husband, Eva embarked on the 'Rainbow Tour' of Europe,

meeting with various **9)** [d][i][ ][n][i][ ][a][r][i][ ][s] and heads of

state. When Eva died in 1952 at the age of 33, Argentina went

into **10)** [ ][o][u][r][ ][i][n][ ] .   **Score** [ ]   **Percentage** [ ] %

Cloze Test 31

Fill in the missing letters to complete the passage below.

We were not too soon, for just as we reached **1)** | s | h | | l | | e | | the sun

went down with startling **2)** | r | a | | i | d | | t | y | , leaving the world

nearly dark, for in these latitudes there is but little

3) | | w | | l | i | g | | t | . So we crept into the cave, which did not appear

to be very big, and **4)** | h | u | | d | l | | n | g | ourselves together for warmth,

swallowed what remained of our brandy—barely a mouthful each—and tried to forget

our **5)** | m | | s | | r | i | | s | in sleep. But the cold was too intense to allow

us to do so, for I am convinced that at this great **6)** | a | l | | i | t | u | | e |

the thermometer cannot have marked less than fourteen or fifteen degrees below

freezing point. What such a temperature meant to us, enervated as we were by

hardship, want of food, and the great heat of the desert, the reader may imagine better

than I can describe. **7)** | S | | f | f | i | | e | it to say that it was something as

near death from **8)** | e | | p | | s | u | r | | as I have ever felt. There we sat

hour after hour through the still and bitter night, feeling the frost wander round and

nip us now in the finger, now in the foot, now in the face. In **9)** | v | | i | |

did we huddle up closer and closer; there was no warmth in our miserable starved

10) | c | a | | c | | s | e | | . Sometimes one of us would drop into an

uneasy slumber for a few minutes, but we could not sleep much, and perhaps this was

fortunate, for if we had I doubt if we should have ever woke again.

Extract from *King Solomon's Mines*
by H. Rider Haggard (1856-1929).

Score | | **Percentage** | | **%**

43

Cloze Test 32

Select the correct words to complete the passage below.

Horatio Nelson was born in Norfolk in 1758. At the age of 12 he joined, as an

1)
- [ ] ordinary
- [ ] merchant
- [ ] experienced

seaman and coxswain, the ship *HMS Raisonnable* under the

2)
- [ ] commital
- [ ] comment
- [ ] command

of his maternal uncle. He was appointed a midshipman shortly

after and began his officer training. He rose rapidly through the **3)**
- [ ] ranks
- [ ] rigging
- [ ] air

and

achieved his own command in 1778. He **4)**
- [ ] benefitted
- [ ] shrank
- [ ] suffered

from seasickness

throughout his entire naval career and from several recurring **5)**
- [ ] bites
- [ ] bouts
- [ ] bales

of

malaria. During a year spent at home in 1783/4, Nelson **6)**
- [ ] contemplated
- [ ] resisted
- [ ] concocted

standing for Parliament but was unable to find a seat. He was given command of the

7)
- [ ] frigate
- [ ] lifeboat
- [ ] submarine

HMS Boreas in 1784 and **8)**
- [ ] stoked
- [ ] repaired
- [ ] set

sail for Antigua. Whilst

there, he met and married Francis Nisbet in 1787 in Nevis, a small

9)
- [ ] mountain
- [ ] island
- [ ] oasis

in the Caribbean Sea. They returned to England and

10)
☐ settled
☐ secured
☐ secluded
in Nelson's home town of Thorpe in Norfolk. He was now in

11)
☐ contention
☐ prison
☐ reserve
, on half pay and **12)**
☐ reluctant
☐ desperate
☐ sad
to be given another

command. Unfortunately, in the **13)**
☐ French
☐ expanding
☐ peacetime
navy there were too few ships

available. He was **14)**
☐ recalled
☐ collected
☐ prised
to be captain of the 64-gun *HMS Agamemnon* in

January 1793, just one month before France **15)**
☐ deployed
☐ deluded
☐ declared
war. In 1794, Nelson

lost the sight in his right eye after being **16)**
☐ wounded
☐ inspected
☐ abandoned
in Corsica and lost his

right arm at the Battle of Santa Cruz de Tenerife in 1797. Nelson was

17)
☐ appointed
☐ celebrated
☐ conscripted
commander-in-chief of the Mediterranean Fleet and took

18)
☐ notice
☐ command
☐ cover
of his most famous ship, *HMS Victory*, in 1803. At the Battle

of Trafalgar in 1805, Nelson was **19)**
☐ seriously
☐ slightly
☐ mortally
wounded by a shot from an

enemy sniper. His body was returned to England to be **20)**
☐ exhibited
☐ exhumed
☐ interred
in

St Paul's Cathedral.

Score ☐ **Percentage** ☐ **%**

Cloze Test 33

Fill in the missing letters to complete the passage below.

Spring opened late that year, but the Summer, when it came, was a warm one. Katy

felt the heat very much. She could not change her seat and follow the

1) | b | | e | e | | e | about from window to window as other people could. The

long burning days left her weak and 2) | p | a | | c | h | e | | . She hung her

head, and seemed to 3) | | i | l | t | like the flowers in the garden-beds. Indeed

she was worse off than they, for every evening Alexander gave them a watering

with the hose, while nobody was able to bring a watering-pot and pour out what she

needed – a shower of cold, fresh air. It wasn't easy to be good-humoured under these

4) | | i | r | c | | m | s | | a | | c | e | | , and one could hardly have

blamed Katy if she had sometimes forgotten her

5) | r | | s | o | | u | t | | | n | | and been cross and

6) | f | r | | t | f | | l | . But she didn't – not very often. Now and then bad

days came, when she was discouraged and 7) | f | | | r | l | | | | n | . But

Katy's long year of schooling had taught her self-control, and, as a general thing, her

8) | d | i | | c | o | | | o | r | | | s | were borne patiently. She could not

help growing pale and thin, however, and Papa saw with concern that, as the summer

went on, she became too 9) | l | | n | g | | i | | | to read, or study, or sew, and

just sat hour after hour, with folded hands, 10) | g | | z | | n | | wistfully out

of the window.

Extract from *What Katy Did*
by Susan Coolidge (1835-1905).

Score | | Percentage | % |

Cloze Test 34

Choose the correct words from the word bank below to complete the passage.

gained	circumnavigate	leg	cropped	determined
altitude	aviators	airfield	fund	contended

Amelia Mary Earhart was born on July 24, 1897. When she was 23 years old, she and her father visited an **1)** _____ and she was taken up in an aircraft for a ten minute flight that would change her life. After that flight she said, "I knew I had to fly." She became **2)** _____ to learn to fly and worked in a variety of jobs to **3)** _____ her lessons. She purchased a leather flying jacket and had her hair **4)** _____ short in the style of female **5)** _____ of the time. She purchased a second-hand, bright yellow biplane, which she nicknamed *The Canary*. Even before she **6)** _____ her pilot's licence, she set a women's world **7)** _____ record, taking *The Canary* up to 14,000 feet. At the age of 34, Earhart began to attempt the first solo flight by a female pilot across the Atlantic. She took off from Harbour Grace, Newfoundland, taking with her a copy of the *Telegraph-Journal* dated 20th May, 1932, to confirm the date of the attempt, intending to land in Paris. After a flight lasting 14 hours, 56 minutes during which she **8)** _____ with strong northerly winds, icy conditions and mechanical problems, Earhart landed in a field at Culmore, north of Derry, Northern Ireland. In 1937, Earhart and her crew member, Fred Noonan, began their attempt to **9)** _____ the globe. Having completed 22,000 miles they set off to cross the Pacific on the final **10)** _____ but the aircraft disappeared. The two bodies and their aircraft were never recovered.

Score ____ Percentage ____ %

Cloze Test 35

Select the correct words to complete the passage below.

We walk past them every day; they have **1)**
☐ polluted
☐ granted
☐ graced
our streets for over 150

years; their use and necessity has not changed in all that time. It is **2)**
☐ estimated
☐ censored
☐ contorted

that there are over 100,000 **3)**
☐ searching
☐ stalling
☐ surviving
red post boxes in the United Kingdom.

This number includes the **4)**
☐ unsighted
☐ ubiquitous
☐ uncertain
red pillar box, with a black base, wall

boxes and lamp boxes. The latter are **5)**
☐ mounted
☐ missing
☐ mailed
on a post. They may also be

found all over the world in most **6)**
☐ fastidious
☐ worthy
☐ former
nations of the British Empire,

members of the Commonwealth of Nations and British **7)**
☐ overseas
☐ local
☐ ancient
territories.

The first pillar boxes were **8)**
☐ excreted
☐ excluded
☐ erected
in St. Helier, Jersey in 1852, just 12 years

after the introduction of the **9)**
☐ expensive
☐ useless
☐ uniform
penny post and the penny black, which

was the first **10)**
☐ ad hoc
☐ adhesive
☐ addressed
postage stamp. These pillar boxes were painted green

and it was not until 1874 that the now **11)**
☐ familiar
☐ faded
☐ feasible
red hue was adopted. On the

12)
- [ ] contrary
- [ ] rebound
- [ ] mainland

, the first pillar boxes were **13)**
- [ ] installed
- [ ] stolen
- [ ] damaged

in Carlisle in 1853,

with London having to wait a further two years before five were placed in the

14)
- [ ] provinces
- [ ] countryside
- [ ] capital

. Since 1905, the traditional **15)**
- [ ] cylindrical
- [ ] pygmy
- [ ] octagonal

pillar boxes

are made of cast iron. In more recent times, pillar boxes found in secure indoor

locations, such as **16)**
- [ ] carparks
- [ ] footpaths
- [ ] supermarkets

and shopping malls, are constructed from

glass fibre or plastic. Each pillar box has a **17)**
- [ ] unique
- [ ] bent
- [ ] clear

Chubb lock with its

individual key. There are no **18)**
- [ ] stubby
- [ ] skeleton
- [ ] bright

keys and postal workers have to carry

a **19)**
- [ ] clutch
- [ ] gaggle
- [ ] bunch

of keys with them to **20)**
- [ ] empty
- [ ] fill
- [ ] chase

all the boxes on their round.

Score [ ] Percentage [ ] %

Cloze Test 36

Choose the correct words from the word bank below to complete the passage.

scarce	**struck**	**throb**	**haul**	**bewilderment**
giddy	**clutched**	**violently**	**tugged**	**clambering**

In a moment I was **1)** _____ by several hands, and there was no

mistaking that they were trying to **2)** _____ me back. I struck another

light, and waved it in their dazzled faces. You can **3)** _____ imagine

how nauseatingly inhuman they looked - those pale, chinless faces and great, lidless,

pinkish-grey eyes! - as they stared in their blindness and **4)** _____ . But I

did not stay to look, I promise you: I retreated again, and when my second match had

ended, I **5)** _____ my third. It had almost burned through when I reached

the opening into the shaft. I lay down on the edge, for the **6)** _____ of

the great pump below made me **7)** _____ . Then I felt sideways for the

projecting hooks, and, as I did so, my feet were grasped from behind, and I was

violently **8)** _____ backward. I lit my last match ... and it incontinently

went out. But I had my hand on the climbing bars now, and, kicking

9) _____ , I disengaged myself from the clutches of the Morlocks and

was speedily **10)** _____ up the shaft, while they stayed peering and

blinking up at me: all but one little wretch who followed me for some way, and well

nigh secured my boot as a trophy.

Extract from *The Time Machine* by H. G. Wells (1866-1946).

Score ☐ Percentage ☐ %

Cloze Test 37

Fill in the missing letters to complete the passage below.

The rooks are **1)** | b | u | | l | d | i | n | | on the trees;

They build there every **2)** | s | | r | i | n | | :

"Caw, caw," is all they say,

For none of them can sing.

They're up before the break of day,

And up till late at night;

For they must **3)** | l | a | | o | u | | busily

As long as it is **4)** | l | i | | | t | .

And many a **5)** | c | | o | o | k | | d | stick they bring,

And many a slender **6)** | | w | | g | ,

And many a **7)** | t | | f | t | of moss, until

Their nests are round and big.

"Caw, caw!" Oh, what a noise

They make in **8)** | | a | i | n | | weather!

Good children always **9)** | s | | e | a | k | by turns,

But rooks all talk **10)** | | o | g | | t | h | | r | .

The Rooks by Jane Euphemia Browne (1811-1898).

Score | | **Percentage** | % |

Cloze Test 38

Choose the correct words from the word bank below to complete the passage.

auspices	**contracting**	**solidarity**	**safety**	**concealed**
smuggle	**tolerated**	**creating**	**permit**	**accomplices**
pretext	**codename**	**execution**	**typhus**	**ingenious**
nominated	**tortured**	**enormous**	**honours**	**occupation**

Irena Sendler was born as Irena Krzyżanowska in 1910 near Warsaw in Poland. Her father, Dr. Stanisław Krzyżanowski, was a doctor and died from **1)** _____ he contracted while treating patients other doctors refused to treat for fear of **2)** _____ the disease; among them many were Jews. After her father's death, Jewish leaders offered to help her mother pay for Irena's education.

During the German **3)** _____ of Poland in World War II, Irena lived in Warsaw. She was employed by the Social Welfare Department and was given a special **4)** _____ to enter the Warsaw Ghetto to check for signs of typhus. The occupying army feared the disease would spread beyond the Ghetto.

She began aiding Jews soon after the German invasion in 1939. In August 1943, Irena, known by her nom de guerre: '*Jolanta*', was **5)** _____ by Żegota to head its Jewish children's section. She led a group of co-workers to help Jewish families by **6)** _____ more than 3,000 false documents for them.

Żegota was the **7)** _____ for The Council to Aid Jews, which operated under the **8)** _____ of the Polish Government in Exile. The organisation, the only one of its kind in any country in Nazi-occupied Europe, helped the country's Jews and found places of **9)** _____ for them in occupied Poland. Irena worked with a group of about thirty volunteers, who were mostly women.

Assisting the Jewish community in any way was extremely dangerous and undertaken at **10)** _____ risk. Not only was the person involved threatened with the death penalty, but so were their entire family or household. It was only in Poland where such action was punishable by death.

The main purpose of the organisation was to **11)** _____ babies and small children out of the Ghetto. This was achieved using ambulances and trams and by using other **12)** _____ methods: babies were even **13)** _____ in packages, tool boxes and suitcases. The rescued children were placed with Polish families, orphanages and convents. By cooperating with the RGO, which was a Polish relief organisation **14)** _____ by the occupying forces, Irena visited the Ghetto under the **15)** _____ of inspecting sanitary conditions. During these visits, Irena wore a Star of David as a sign of **16)** _____ with the Jewish people and so as not to draw attention to herself.

In 1943, the Gestapo arrested and severely **17)** _____ Irena. They beat her brutally, fracturing her feet and legs. Her refusal to betray any of her **18)** _____ , or the children they rescued, resulted in her being sentenced to death by firing squad. She was saved from this fate when Żegota bribed the guards on the way to her **19)** _____ .

After the war Irena was awarded numerous **20)** _____ ; among them was the Nobel Peace Prize in 2009.

Irena Sendler died in Warsaw on 12 May 2008, aged 98.

Score [ ] **Percentage** [%]

Cloze Test 39

Select the correct words to complete the passage below.

Perhaps the first use of forensic science may be **1)**
| □ attributed |
| □ rushed |
| □ alluded |
to Archimedes. He

was asked to **2)**
| □ ascertain |
| □ try |
| □ gamble |
whether a goldsmith had **3)**
| □ manufactured |
| □ polished |
| □ substituted |
silver

for pure gold he used to make a crown for King Hiero II. Archimedes

4)
| □ overcame |
| □ compounded |
| □ strained |
the problem of how this could be achieved without having to

melt down the crown to measure the **5)**
| □ frequency |
| □ length |
| □ density |
of the material. Instead, he

6)
| □ preserved |
| □ busted |
| □ repealed |
the undamaged crown by using the law of displacement to prove

the goldsmith's dishonesty. Forensic science covers a multitude of **7)**
| □ sins |
| □ disciplines |
| □ descendants |

including toxicology and ballistics, anthropometry, fingerprinting, photography and

many others. **8)**
| □ Modern |
| □ Dismal |
| □ Caustic |
forensic science dates from the 18th century when

9)
| □ conscious |
| □ crowded |
| □ criminal |
investigation became a more evidence-based, **10)**
| □ random |
| □ raucous |
| □ rational |

procedure. Prior to this, extreme measures, such as using torture to extract

11)
- [ ] complaints
- [ ] converts
- [ ] confessions

, and belief in the power of the occult and witchcraft

12)
- [ ] gained
- [ ] cursed
- [ ] used

to influence the court's decisions. In 1784, forensic evidence in the

trial of John Toms led to his **13)**
- [ ] conviction
- [ ] passion
- [ ] eviction

for murder. Newspaper found in the

head wound of the victim matched that **14)**
- [ ] enterred
- [ ] leaking
- [ ] found

in Toms' pocket. It had

been used by Toms to make a pistol wad in the weapon he used to **15)**
- [ ] shoot
- [ ] stab
- [ ] stifle

his

victim. In 1858, fingerprinting to **16)**
- [ ] identify
- [ ] annoy
- [ ] allude

criminal suspects was

17)
- [ ] busted
- [ ] poached
- [ ] advocated

by Sir William Herschel, who worked for the Indian Civil Service

and used **18)**
- [ ] elbow
- [ ] knee
- [ ] thumb

prints on documents to prove their

19)
- [ ] heritage
- [ ] authenticity
- [ ] usefulness

. More recently, in 1984, the scientist Alec Jeffreys

20)
- [ ] pioneered
- [ ] banned
- [ ] pretended

the use of DNA profiling in forensic science.

Score [   ] Percentage [%]

Cloze Test 40

Choose the correct words from the word bank below to complete the passage.

developed	**communicate**	**impaired**	**advocate**	**frustrated**
contracted	**breakthrough**	**directed**	**activist**	**vocabulary**

When she was born in Alabama in 1880, Helen Keller's sight and hearing were

normal. When she was 19 months old she **1)** _____ an illness, thought to

be scarlet fever or meningitis, which left her deaf and blind. She began to use signs

to **2)** _____ , and the family cook's six-year-old daughter was able to

understand them. Helen **3)** _____ these signs and, by the time she was

seven, she had a **4)** "_____" of more than 60, which she used in the

family home. Helen's mother sought help for her daughter and was

5) _____ to the Perkins Institute for the Blind. 20-year-old Anne

Sullivan, a former pupil of the Institute, who was herself visually

6) _____ , became Helen's instructor. She began to spell words onto

Helen's hand, beginning with "d-o-l-l", for the doll she had given her as a present.

Not understanding that every object had a name, Helen became extremely

7) _____ . The **8)** _____ came when Anne ran water over

one of Helen's hands while spelling out the word on the other. Helen Keller became

a political **9)** _____ and a world famous speaker. She died in 1968 and is

remembered as an **10)** _____ for people with disabilities.

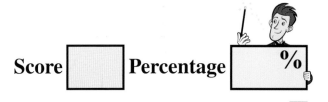

Score ☐ Percentage ☐ %

Answers

Test 1
1) rose
2) brink
3) barley
4) float
5) swan
6) Sailing
7) mellow
8) flowers
9) clouds
10) twilight

Test 2
1) founder
2) pursued
3) lifting
4) promoted
5) revered
6) learnt
7) manual
8) organisations
9) suit
10) ideas
11) instalments
12) approximately
13) en route
14) engaged
15) sensation
16) donated
17) Jamboree
18) acclaimed
19) bears
20) trail

Test 3
1) original
2) credited
3) efficiency
4) ingenuity
5) employed

6) adaptation
7) hauled
8) aptitude
9) bankrupt
10) exploit

Test 4
1) nickname
2) knowledge
3) carried
4) criminal
5) experience
6) enlisted
7) rigging
8) travelling
9) sorted
10) stole

Test 5
1) prototypes
2) treaty
3) equivalent
4) aspirations
5) technological
6) maiden
7) supersonic
8) mankind
9) inclement
10) observed
11) instrumentation
12) thundered
13) spontaneous
14) visibility
15) manually
16) uneventfully
17) inoperative
18) withdrawn
19) magnificent
20) genius

Test 6
1) reserves
2) prospecting
3) relied
4) consumption
5) commence
6) provided
7) swelled
8) coffers
9) extracted
10) conclusion

Test 7
1) courted
2) churches
3) rode
4) buttercups
5) cats
6) worried
7) baby
8) crown
9) world
10) blunders

Test 8
1) unpleasant
2) disagreeable
3) abhorred
4) liberty
5) hesitate
6) irritated
7) humane
8) berated
9) sarcastic
10) rector
11) circumstances
12) pressing
13) dreaded
14) villainous
15) retailed

Answers

16) honest
17) village
18) intimate
19) language
20) agreeable

Test 9
1) discoveries
2) complained
3) sour
4) growth
5) patented
6) pursue
7) immunising
8) trial
9) mauled
10) popularly

Test 10
1) diseases
2) developed
3) established
4) husbandry
5) thoroughly
6) sufficient
7) microbes
8) utensils
9) sterilising
10) germs

Test 11
1) consideration
2) generator
3) extraction
4) commercial
5) plant
6) invented
7) granted
8) implemented
9) drawn
10) sustainable

11) capacity
12) utlise
13) heated
14) imports
15) polluted
16) crust
17) decaying
18) conduction
19) natural
20) active

Test 12
1) skilful
2) plain
3) halt
4) prostration
5) stupefied
6) effects
7) fumes
8) disturbed
9) fate
10) inevitably

Test 13
1) sting
2) evolved
3) predator
4) lethal
5) toxins
6) capability
7) inject
8) fangs
9) allergic
10) administered

Test 14
1) dying
2) peasant
3) prying
4) treasure
5) grave

6) reward
7) sinks
8) tedious
9) straight
10) vineyard
11) sift
12) inclined
13) autumn
14) vintage
15) quoth
16) legacy
17) purple
18) digging
19) reflect
20) labour

Test 15
1) derived
2) mechanical
3) topics
4) essential
5) tubing
6) membrane
7) paramount
8) projection
9) scanning
10) structures

Test 16
1) pillows
2) beside
3) soldiers
4) uniforms
5) sometimes
6) brought
7) planted
8) giant
9) dale
10) counterpane

Answers

Test 17
1) towards
2) exceedingly
3) naked
4) sand
5) apparition
6) rising
7) impression
8) observe
9) exactly
10) thither
11) innumerable
12) confused
13) fortification
14) terrified
15) mistaking
16) stump
17) describe
18) affrighted
19) fancy
20) whimsies

Test 18
1) contained
2) disturbingly
3) compulsory
4) considerate
5) influence
6) tiredness
7) stretch
8) security
9) mandatory
10) annually

Test 19
1) renowned
2) transfusion
3) treatment
4) witnessed
5) resolved

6) syringe
7) donor
8) recipient
9) accomplished
10) devised

Test 20
1) perpetrated
2) Roundhead
3) acted
4) confiscated
5) villainous
6) knack
7) befriended
8) accomplices
9) stomach
10) stuffed
11) apprehended
12) Inexplicably
13) violent
14) granted
15) speculated
16) revenue
17) theories
18) embarrass
19) exhumed
20) faked

Test 21
1) epicentre
2) attributed
3) neighbourhood
4) tumbled
5) considerable
6) activity
7) inhabitants
8) ferocity
9) fault
10) underpin

Test 22
1) bestowed
2) conspicuous
3) distinction
4) appropriate
5) founding
6) Sovereign
7) Recipients
8) medallion
9) motto
10) politicians

Test 23
1) haunt
2) whitewashed
3) beaming
4) may
5) sunbeams
6) woody
7) trunks
8) shaded
9) cast
10) darkness
11) encountered
12) disbeliever
13) foray
14) galloped
15) turned
16) clap
17) jockey
18) overtaken
19) punch
20) bolted

Test 24
1) harrowing
2) accumulated
3) avalanche
4) debris
5) engulfing

Answers

6) nestling
7) shrouded
8) frantic
9) instability
10) criticised

Test 25
1) misconception
2) affordable
3) conveyance
4) assembly
5) repetitive
6) eager
7) adequately
8) committed
9) democratic
10) injustice

Test 26
1) portrayed
2) plaques
3) resembles
4) popular
5) sharply
6) superseded
7) constitutes
8) counterparts
9) respectively
10) suffix
11) gradually
12) identical
13) increased
14) evolved
15) revolutionary
16) proportions
17) tension
18) construction
19) obviated
20) debatable

Test 27
1) persuasions
2) movement
3) scream
4) writhing
5) grievous
6) gauged
7) folly
8) companion
9) knelt
10) breath

Test 28
1) emigrated
2) stylish
3) complexion
4) manufacture
5) pungent
6) accomplishment
7) concept
8) donning
9) faltered
10) perceived

Test 29
1) gentleman
2) able
3) bade
4) grave
5) fidgety
6) giggles
7) Swings
8) tilts
9) child
10) rude
11) cloth
12) matters
13) fret

14) tumbling
15) disgrace
16) Fairly
17) terrible
18) snapped
19) bare
20) dinner

Test 30
1) rural
2) diminutive
3) formal
4) contracted
5) stability
6) considerable
7) demonstrations
8) landslide
9) dignitaries
10) mourning

Test 31
1) shelter
2) rapidity
3) twilight
4) huddling
5) miseries
6) altitude
7) Suffice
8) exposure
9) vain
10) carcases

Test 32
1) ordinary
2) command
3) ranks
4) suffered
5) bouts

6) contemplated
7) frigate
8) set
9) island
10) settled
11) reserve
12) desperate
13) peacetime
14) recalled
15) declared
16) wounded
17) appointed
18) command
19) mortally
20) interred

Test 33
1) breeze
2) parched
3) wilt
4) circumstances
5) resolutions
6) fretful
7) forlorn
8) discomforts
9) languid
10) gazing

Test 34
1) airfield
2) determined
3) fund
4) cropped
5) aviators
6) gained
7) altitude
8) contended
9) circumnavigate
10) leg

Test 35
1) graced
2) estimated
3) surviving
4) ubiquitous
5) mounted
6) former
7) overseas
8) erected
9) uniform
10) adhesive
11) familiar
12) mainland
13) installed
14) capital
15) cylindrical
16) supermarkets
17) unique
18) skeleton
19) bunch
20) empty

Test 36
1) clutched
2) haul
3) scarce
4) bewilderment
5) struck
6) throb
7) giddy
8) tugged
9) violently
10) clambering

Test 37
1) building
2) spring
3) labour
4) light
5) crooked

6) twig
7) tuft
8) rainy
9) speak
10) together

Test 38
1) typhus
2) contracting
3) occupation
4) permit
5) nominated
6) creating
7) codename
8) auspices
9) safety
10) enormous
11) smuggle
12) ingenious
13) concealed
14) tolerated
15) pretext
16) solidarity
17) tortured
18) accomplices
19) execution
20) honours

Test 39
1) attributed
2) ascertain
3) substituted
4) overcame
5) density
6) preserved
7) disciplines
8) Modern
9) criminal
10) rational

Answers

11) confessions
12) used
13) conviction
14) found
15) shoot
16) identify
17) advocated
18) thumb
19) authenticity
20) pioneered

Test 40
1) contracted
2) communicate
3) developed
4) vocabulary
5) directed
6) impaired
7) frustrated
8) breakthrough
9) activist
10) advocate

PROGRESS CHARTS

Test	Mark	%
1		
2		
3		
4		
5		
6		
7		
8		
9		
10		
11		
12		
13		
14		
15		
16		
17		
18		
19		
20		

Test	Mark	%
21		
22		
23		
24		
25		
26		
27		
28		
29		
30		
31		
32		
33		
34		
35		
36		
37		
38		
38		
40		

Overall Percentage %

CERTIFICATE OF

ACHIEVEMENT

This certifies

_____

has successfully completed

11+ Verbal Reasoning
Year 5–7 Cloze

TESTBOOK **2**

Overall percentage
score achieved

%

Comment _____

_____

Signed _____

(teacher/parent/guardian)

Date _____